# The Twins

## Clare Helen Welsh

### Illustrated by Andrea Castro Naranjo

Schofield&Sims

Jasper and Meg were twins. They were on a camping trip with Mum.

Jasper was the best at fishing. He had the longest fishing rod.

But when Meg hooked her fish,
it dragged her in.

Splash!

"Oops," sniggered Jasper.

Meg was the best at constructing dens. She had the strongest sticks.

But Jasper was afraid of the dark.
When Meg turned out the lights,
he started to weep.

"Oops," sniggered Meg.

Mum got cross. "Stop this sniggering!" she said. "Having a twin is a good thing. It can be like having a best pal!"

"Quick, let's run!" grinned Meg.
"Wait! You are quicker than me!
I cannot keep up!" puffed Jasper.

Soon the twins were lost. They looked
for Mum but she was not there.

Jasper had the longest fishing rod.
Meg had the strongest sticks.

Soon the twins were back with Mum.
"We were lost! We looked for you!"
Jasper exclaimed.

"Oops!" grinned Mum. "But do you see? Now you are best pals!" Jasper and Meg agreed.